MODERN KID PRESS

Third Grade Reading Comprehension Workbook

Stories to Share

THIS BOOK BELONGS TO:

_____
. . . .
_____

Want free goodies?!

Email us at

modernkidpress@gmail.com

Title the email
"Grade 3 Reading Comprehension"
and we'll send some goodies your way!

Follow us on Instagram!
@modernkidpress

Questions & Customer Service:
Email us at modernkidpress@gmailcom!

Stories to Share: Reading Comprehension Grade 3

Written by Jamie McGillian. Illustrations by Erin Gennow. Art direction by Jacy Corral.

Table of Contents

Dear Caregiver,

Welcome to *The Third Grade Reading Comprehension Workbook: Stories to Share*, a mix of material to boost reading comprehension skills. This collection will enhance social and emotional growth, foster a love of literature and informational texts, and will help keep your student reading, writing, and thinking. The content is fresh, providing relevant topics that are pertinent and challenging to primary students. Your student can work independently or with a buddy. Talk with your student about each passage for enhanced comprehension. Practice discussing the elements of a story, expressing opinions, and making connections.

If you have any questions or concerns, feel free to reach out to us at modernkidpress@gmail.com.

Happy reading!

— Jamie McGillian & The Modern Kid Press team

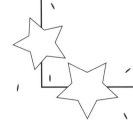

Reading Comprehension

SKILLS

After your child works through all of the stories, they will be a ROCK STAR in the following skills!

- Ask and answer questions from the text

- Describe character's traits and motivations

- Determine cause and effect

- Determine fact and opinion

- Determine the meaning of words and phrases as they are used in a text

- Distinguish a point of view separate from narrator

- Distinguish literal from nonliteral language

- Expand vocabulary

- Explain character's motivation

- Explain how the words in a story create mood or setting

- Find central message

- Identify main Ideas

- Read at grade level with purpose and understanding

- Recount text details

- Recount folktales

- Refer to story parts

- Sequencing

- Text comprehension

- Use illustrations to find key details

- Use text features to locate key information

Look for this ribbon on each story listing the corresponding Common Core standards. An explanation of each standard can be found on page 103.

Missy and the Scarf

It was a busy morning for Maxie, Maddy, and Missy. They were baking mini loaves of banana bread and wrapping them in colorful plastic and ribbons. As the girls washed their hands, Mama yelled, "Package from Auntie Maggie!"

The girls ran from the sink with their hands still dripping wet. Mama was holding a box.

Auntie Maggie loved sending the girls gifts and the girls loved receiving them.

The girls gathered around Mama as she opened the box. Inside was a note from Auntie Maggie. Mama read it out loud.

"Dear Maxie, Maddy, and Missy, I have made a scarf for each one of you. Please wear it to stay warm this winter when you play in the snow. The scarf with the little rainbows is for big sister, Maxie."

Maxie jumped in the air. "I love rainbows!"

"The scarf with the tiny wildflowers is for middle sister, Maddy."

"I love wildflowers!" Maddy twirled in the air.

"The scarf with the teeny strawberries is for little sister, Missy."

"Strawberries?" said Missy. "Strawberries? Is this a joke?" Missy made a face that looked like she was smelling something extra yucky.

"Missy, the strawberries on your scarf are not real," Mama said.

"But they make me think of real strawberries. Mushy, squishy, and disgusting," Missy said.

"You are being silly!" Mama said.

Maxie put on her rainbow scarf.

Maddy put on her flower scarf.

Missy made an angry face. "Well, I am absolutely not wearing a strawberry scarf!" Missy said.

Then Maxie said, "You are just being difficult, Missy!"

Then Maddy said, "Yeah, difficult!"

"How can anyone expect me to wear a scarf with strawberries on it?" Missy said, shaking her head wildly.

Then Mama said, "Enough strawberry talk!"

Then the doorbell rang.

It was. . . .

"Surprise!" yelled Auntie Maggie.

Auntie Maggie looked at Maxie and smiled at her in her new rainbow scarf. Then she looked at Maddy and smiled at her in her new wildflower scarf.

Auntie Maggie looked at Missy and asked, "Where is your strawberry scarf, Missy?"

"Strawberries are terrible. They are mushy. They make your fingers red," said Missy.

"Well, that may be, but those strawberries are not real!" said Auntie Maggie.

Maxie and Maddy were tired of waiting for Missy to put on her strawberry scarf.

"Missy, how do you feel about teddy bears?" asked Auntie Maggie.

"Teddy bears? I love teddy bears. They are my second-favorite thing," said Missy.

"What's your first favorite thing?" asked Maxie.

"Stars, of course!" said Missy.

"Since when?" asked Maddy.

"Since the beginning of time!" answered Missy.

Auntie Maggie dipped her hand into her bag and pulled out a scarf with teddy bears all over it.

"How did you know I love teddy bears, Auntie Maggie?" asked Missy, taking the teddy bear scarf and wrapping it around her neck.

"Well," said Auntie Maggie. "It was just a hunch."

Now the three sisters were ready to play outside in their new scarves.

Missy looked at the teddy bears on her scarf and smiled, as the girls began playing Hide and Seek.

STORY 1 QUESTIONS

After you read Story 1, answer the questions below.

1. Who is the main character?

    _____

2. Where does the story take place?

    _____

3. How many sisters does Missy have?

    _____

4. Why does Missy refuse to wear the first scarf?

    _____

5. Do you think Missy is a picky person? Why or why not?

    _____

6. **What happened when?** Put these events from the story in the order
    that they happened. One is done for you.

    6 The girls began playing Hide and Seek.

    ◯ Missy put on her scarf.

    ◯ Auntie Maggie showed up.

    ◯ A package came.

    ◯ The girls were washing their hands.

    ◯ The girls were making banana bread.

 For Fun! Here is a picture of Missy. Draw her teddy bear scarf.

Let's Work Together

A pencil and a crayon lived in the pocket of a neon-blue backpack.

The pencil said, "Look at me! I am cool."

The crayon spun around and said, "Well, I am fun and colorful."

"Pencils are better than crayons!" chanted the pencil.

"That is not a nice thing to say," said the crayon.

"But I am a pencil. I have a point," said the pencil.

That made the crayon feel sad.

"How can you say that to me?" asked the crayon.

"Because I am a pencil!" declared the pencil.

"Well," said the crayon, "I am a crayon!"

The pencil looked at the crayon.

The crayon looked at the pencil.

"I make lines and shapes," said the crayon, proudly.

"I write stories and lists," said the pencil, proudly.

"Yes, but I am colorful," said the crayon.

That made the pencil feel sad.

The pencil and the crayon began to argue.

"I am better than you!" said the pencil.

"I am better than you!" said the crayon.

Just then, the teacher spoke.

"Students, it is time to take out your pencils and your crayons. You will write your story with your pencil. You will draw a picture with your crayon," said the teacher.

The pencil and the crayon got busy.

What they created was truly beautiful.

Later, the pencil and the crayon agreed that they made a good team.

STORY 2 QUESTIONS

After you read Story 2, answer the questions below.

1.   Why does the pencil think he is so great?

_____

_____

_____

2.   Why does the crayon think he is so great?

_____

_____

_____

3.   Which is more important to you, a pencil or a crayon? Explain your reasoning.

_____

_____

_____

4.   What makes a good team?

_____

_____

_____

5.   Use your imagination with a pencil and a crayon to fill the space below.

Make Time for Positive Messages

Have you ever cheered for yourself or given yourself a high-five? It may seem strange to actually talk to yourself, but just hear me out. You know you better than anyone, right? You are your biggest fan. That's the way it is with me. I am my biggest fan!

Let's say I bump into a table when kids are watching and I feel embarrassed, or I am having trouble with homework and I start to doubt my intelligence. I stay strong and ready for most challenges with my daily positive messages, or affirmations. I have worked out a routine. Here's what I do:

Find a quiet space.

Take a few deep breaths.

Think about all the wonderful parts of my life.

Begin affirming.

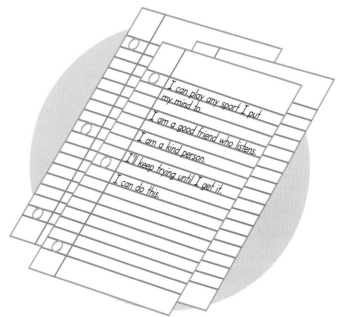

"Good morning, Mr. Amazing!"

"Do I need a twinkle to go with that star?" I wink at myself.

"I got this!" I say out loud and do a little dance move. Then I go big with, "I have a strong mind and body. I am smart and I can do anything I set my mind to!"

I repeat that last line a few times in a serious voice, and then I take five deep breaths.

I feel like a new person. These happy statements help me feel comfortable, secure, and powerful in my own skin. Try it and you will see how telling yourself positive messages can help you feel great about yourself!

STORY 3 QUESTIONS

After you read Story 3, answer the questions below.

1.   Who is the narrator's biggest fan?

_____

2.   What does the narrator do just before he takes a few deep breaths?

_____

3.   What do you think the narrator means when he says he feels comfortable in his own skin?

_____

_____

_____

4.   Many people recite daily positive messages, or affirmations, to help build confidence and relieve stress. Is this something you might try? Why or why not?

_____

_____

_____

5.   Write your own positive messages to yourself here:

_____

_____

_____

How to Start a Healthy Habit
Try saying positive messages twice a day: when you wake up and before you go to sleep. Repeat each message five to ten times. Listen to your voice, focus on the words, and believe your own message. Develop a daily routine. Try not to skip any days. Be patient. It may take some time before you feel more confident and relaxed.

Sassy and Ever

A Sassafras tree with colorful leaves stood close to a tree with dark green leaves called an Evergreen. The trees stood next to one another in a beautiful park.

Sassafras, who was nicknamed Sassy, and Evergreen, who was nicknamed Ever, heard laughter and young voices.

"What is all the noise?" asked the sleepy Ever.

Sassy laughed and said, "Wake up, Ever, the children are here!"

When Sassy saw the children running around, she shook her leaves. They shimmered in the gentle wind.

"Wow, would you look at those leaves? The colors are amazing!" a small human with red hair shouted.

Sassy was filled with pride.

She loved that the children had come to admire her leaves.

Ever had leaves that stayed green all year. How boring! Ever thought to herself.

Sassy was telling Ever that the children seemed bigger than last year.

"We have grown, too," added Sassy.

Ever was interested in this. "We have?"

"Our trunks have grown wider. Our branches are longer and fuller. We are big, strong trees!"

This news delighted Ever.

"We have grown, Sassy!" Ever said. "I can feel it in my roots!"

The children gathered around Sassy's branches, holding their sketch books and markers.

"They have come to draw you," said Ever.

Sassy beamed.

"It's not fair!" Ever muttered.

Ever wished for colorful leaves. If she had them, she too could dazzle the children.

Sassy felt sad for Ever, but happy for herself. It was weird to feel both happy and sad at the same time.

A boy pointed to Ever, and said, "This tree looks so bright and green. It makes me feel calm."

He sat under Ever to eat his lunch. A group of children followed him.

Now Ever was happy.

Sassy was happy, too.

"They came to see your changing leaves, Sassy," said Ever.

"But they are sitting under your branches, looking at your leaves, Ever," said Sassy.

The two trees realized that they each had their own gifts.

That made them both happy.

STORY 4 ACTIVITIES

After you read Story 4, complete the activities below.

1. **Fact or Opinion?**

   What is the difference between fact and opinion? If you read a statement that you believe is true, and it can be proven, it is a fact. If you read a statement that reflects the opinion of someone, but it cannot really be proven, it is an opinion.

   Read each statement below to determine what is fact or opinion. Write F for fact and O for opinion on the lines.

   _____ A Sassafras tree can have colored leaves.

   _____ Evergreens are the most beautiful trees.

   _____ The leaves on Evergreen trees are always green.

   _____ Most children prefer trees with colorful leaves.

   _____ Fall is the most wonderful time for trees to show off.

   _____ Sitting under a Sassafras can improve your mood.

2. **Write 2 facts here about trees.**

   Example: Trees provide shade.

   _____

   _____

3. **Write 1 opinion about trees.**

   Example: Sitting under a tree is a great way to read a book.

   _____

   _____

4. **Fact or Opinion?**

   Read each statement below to determine what is fact or opinion. Write F for fact and O for opinion on the lines.

   _____ Tree populations are declining.

   _____ Trees produce oxygen.

   _____ Trees with red leaves look best.

   _____ Trees should be planted in the early morning.

   _____ When planting trees, always wear gardening gloves.

STORY 5 | # Willow and Ma

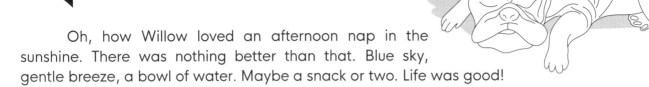

Oh, how Willow loved an afternoon nap in the sunshine. There was nothing better than that. Blue sky, gentle breeze, a bowl of water. Maybe a snack or two. Life was good!

But something was not quite right today. Ma did not have her usual energy. She was not humming songs from the good old days, or talking about what to cook for dinner. She was not blowing kisses in Willow's direction.

Did Willow do something wrong? She sulked and snorted in Ma's direction.

"How's my sweet girl?" said Ma, without opening her eyes.

Willow felt hopeful and reached for Ma's foot. She licked and nibbled gently, like she was munching an ear of corn.

"Willow, my sweet girl, it is not time to tickle toes," Ma said, with her eyes shut.

Willow picked up her pink ball and pressed it against Ma's hand with her mouth.

"Sweet girl, I am just too tired to play ball," Ma said, in a drowsy voice.

In their five years together, Ma had never refused a game of chase. Something was most definitely wrong. Willow could feel it in her bones.

Now Willow's tummy was grumbling as Ma slept on her lounge chair. Willow closed her eyes and imagined her and Ma walking together. Willow drifted off to sleep and woke to a familiar voice.

"Wake up, Willow!"

Willow opened her eyes and saw Uncle Mikey.

"Ma is in the hospital!" he said, placing a big bowl of water in front of Willow.

The hospital! Willow couldn't believe it. She pictured Ma's face, as she gulped her water.

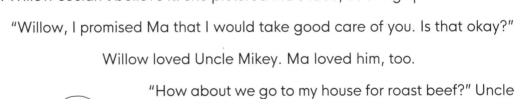

"Willow, I promised Ma that I would take good care of you. Is that okay?"

Willow loved Uncle Mikey. Ma loved him, too.

"How about we go to my house for roast beef?" Uncle Mikey asked.

Roast beef sounded yummy.

"Tomorrow, maybe we can visit Ma in the hospital."

Willow liked that idea a lot.

STORY 5 QUESTIONS

After you read Story 5, answer the questions below.

1.   In the story, what is Willow worried about?
      a. Ma
      b. Uncle Mikey
      c. Roast beef

2.   How did Willow know that something was not right?
      a. Willow was hungry
      b. Ma did not have her usual energy
      c. Willow had a dream

3.   When Willow felt hopeful, what did she do?
      a. barked
      b. fell asleep
      c. licked Ma's foot

4.   Which ending do you like best for this story?
      a. Willow will live with Uncle Mikey.
      b. Willow will live with a new family.
      c. Willow will live in the hospital with Ma.

5.   Choose an ending from below or make up your own.
      a. Willow gets a job at the hospital cheering up patients.
      b. Uncle Mikey and Willow join the circus.
      c. Ma gets out of the hospital and takes Willow out for ice cream.
      d. Willow and Ma take a vacation.
      e. Willow gets a job as a show dog.
      f. Ma has a sweet surprise for Willow.
      g. Write your own ending for the story here:

      _____

      _____

      _____

      _____

      _____

Play It!

What looks like a toy guitar and sounds really cool? No, it's not the guitar or the banjo. It's the ukulele, a tiny instrument that really packs a musical punch. Many musical stars, including Taylor Swift, play the ukulele, and you can, too!

The ukulele has four strings instead of six. It is easy to transport, pick up, and play.

Did you know that the first ukulele came to the United States from Portugal? Known as a *braguinha* or *machete de braga*, it arrived in Hawaii with Portuguese immigrants, who came to Hawaii to work on the sugar plantations.

Ukuleles became popular in Hawaii in 1879, after a ship named Ravenscrag arrived in Honolulu harbor. After the difficult journey, one passenger was so relieved to be safe and sound after a bumpy ride, that he began singing songs of thanks and playing his *braguinha*. The local Hawaiians were captivated by the sound of the instrument. They called it *ukulele*, meaning "jumping flea," to describe how the player's fingers danced quickly over the fretboard. And that's how Hawaii fell in love with the ukulele!

For Fun! Decorate your own ukulele here:

STORY 6 QUESTIONS

After you read Story 6, answer the questions below.

1. According to the passage, which instrument packs a musical punch?
    a. Guitar
    b. Banjo
    c. Ukulele

2. How many strings does the ukulele have?
    a. Four
    b. Six
    c. Thirteen

3. Where did the first ukulele come from?
    a. Hawaii
    b. Portugal
    c. Ravenscrag

4. In what year did ukuleles become popular?
    a. 1879
    b. 1979
    c. 1776

5. What does ukulele mean in Hawaii?
    a. Jumping flea
    b. Guitar
    c. Musical instrument

Chicken Makes Quesadillas!

Once upon a silly time, there was a cute chicken who lived in a house with a boy, a dog, a cat, and a monkey.

Chicken did all the housework and the shopping. Everyone else sat around and played video games.

Chicken said, "I feel like having some cheese quesadillas."

The boy said, "Yum!"

The dog said, "Sounds good!"

The cat said, "I could eat!"

The monkey said, "Oh, yeah!"

So, Chicken got busy.

"Who is going to help spread out the quesadilla?" asked Chicken.

Boy said, "Not me."

Dog said, "No can do."

Cat said, "Can't move from this sunny window."

Monkey said, "Too busy!"

So, Chicken got busy.

"Who is going to help shred the cheese?" asked Chicken.

Boy said, "Not me."

Dog said, "No can do."

Cat said, "Can't move away from this sunny window."

Monkey said, "Too busy."

So, Chicken got busy.

"Who is going to help sprinkle the spinach?" asked Chicken.

Boy said, "Not me."

Dog said, "No can do."

Cat said, "Can't move away from this sunny window."

Monkey said, "Too busy."

So, Chicken got busy.

"Who is going to stir the salsa?" asked Chicken.

Boy said, "Not me."

Dog said, "No can do."

Cat said, "Can't move away from this sunny window."

Monkey said, "Too busy."

So, Chicken got busy.

The quesadillas looked and smelled delicious!

Chicken asked, "Who wants quesadillas?"

Boy said, "I do!"

Dog said, "I do!"

Cat said, "I do!"

Monkey said, "I do!"

Chicken took a big bite of quesadilla and said, "Well, you will have to make your own!"

Chicken sat at the table and ate a delicious lunch while the others watched. Chicken would not share a single bite!

Moral of the Story: Hard work brings rewards. If you don't help, you don't benefit.

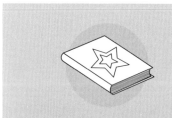

Definition
fable - a short story teaching a moral lesson. The characters are often animals acting as people!

STORY 7 QUESTIONS

After you read Story 7, answer the questions below.

1. Who did all the housework at Chicken's house?
   a. Chicken
   b. Monkey and Chicken
   c. Chicken and the boy

2. What is the main idea of this story?
   a. Chicken is tired of her roommates not taking out the trash.
   b. Everyone has to share the work if they want to eat quesadillas.
   c. A sunny day is great for sitting around indoors.

3. What is a good title for this story?
   a. Teamwork Is the Best Way
   b. Chicken Loves to Cook
   c. Let's Make Salsa

4. Why do you think the other characters will not help Chicken?
   a. They are too tired.
   b. They don't like cheese.
   c. They want Chicken to do all the work.

5. What do you think would make Chicken happy?
   a. If the cat helped with the shopping.
   b. If the boy said "thank you."
   c. If the others would cook and do some of the work.

6. Pretend you are Chicken. What would you want to tell your roommates? Write it here:

   _____

   _____

   _____

   _____

   _____

For Fun! Write your own version of this fable, which is based on *The Little Red Hen*. Include an illustration below.

_____

_____

_____

_____

_____

_____

_____

_____

_____

_____

_____

_____

_____

_____

_____

_____

Large Side of Optimism, Please!

Being optimistic means seeing life in the best light possible. According to scientists, people who are optimistic, who can look on the bright side, have better health, make more money, and have closer relationships with friends and family than those who are not optimistic. The opposite of optimistic is pessimistic, which means seeing the negative side of things. Are you more of an optimist or a pessimist?

It may not always feel right to put on a happy face when we feel sad. But being optimistic means seeing the world through hopeful eyes. Many people find it helpful to keep negative feelings away by staying active. Playing sports or board games like chess, taking art classes, caring for animals, and giving back to your community can keep you feeling optimistic.

Most optimistic people have purpose in their work and home life. Experts say the major difference between optimists and pessimists is not their ability to be happy, but in how they deal with challenges.

STORY 8 QUESTIONS

After you read Story 8, answer the questions below.

1. What does optimism mean?
   a. Putting on a happy face, no matter what.
   b. Seeing life in the best light possible.
   c. Always being happy.

2. What is the opposite of optimistic?
   a. Happy
   b. Silly
   c. Pessimistic

3. According to scientists, what do optimistic people have?
   a. Better health
   b. More bills to pay
   c. Funnier stories

4. What do the experts say is the major difference between optimists and pessimists?
   a. They are the same
   b. How they deal with challenges
   c. Playing chess

STORY 8 ACTIVITY

After you read Story 8, complete the activity below.

For Fun! Are you an optimist or pessimist?

A quiz for everyone in the family!

1. There's a half a glass of lemonade waiting for you. Is it ...
   a. half-full
   b. half-empty

2. The weather person says there is a 50% chance of rain. You think to yourself ...
   a. "There's a good chance we can play outside today."
   b. "It's probably going to pour all day."

3. You are invited to a slumber party. Your first thoughts are ...
   a. "I am going to have so much fun."
   b. "I will never be able to fall asleep."

4. You and your best friend are going shopping, but your friend is bringing another friend that you have not yet met. Your first thought is ...
   a. "It will be fun to meet someone new!"
   b. "I just know I won't like the person."

5. There are four open slots for chess practice, but there are five people, including you. Your first thought is ...
   a. "I hope I get picked to play."
   b. "I'll probably be the one who just gets to watch."

Scoring: For every response that you answer a, give yourself 10 points. If you scored 30 points or higher, good for you! You lean toward being an optimist! If your score was lower than 30, don't worry. You can build your optimism by looking for the bright side.

Dog Wearing a Pizza Box

There was a dog named Ringo.

He loved to play games like bingo.

Ringo ran through the streets,

in the cold and the heat.

He was big,

and he was loud,

but he was really, very sweet.

But Ringo wasn't very patient.

One day, he needed an operation.

The vet made him wear a cone on his head.

And said to him, "Ringo, go home to bed!"

But Ringo wouldn't hear of it.

Plus, the cone was a very bad fit.

Ringo tore it to pieces, and wanted to do more.

So a wild Ringo headed out the door.

He ran into a friendly pizza guy.

Then he ate a delicious pizza pie!

He even took the box.

And ran for the rocks.

He wore the box as his hat.

Can you just imagine that?

STORY 9 QUESTIONS

After you read Story 9, answer the questions below.

1. What is the dog's name?

   _____

2. Is the dog big or small?

   _____

3. Why did the dog go to the vet?

   _____

   _____

4. What did the dog tear to pieces?

   _____

   _____

5. What did the dog eat?

   _____

   _____

6. What was on the dog's head?

   _____

   _____

RL.3.1
RL.3.2
RL.3.3
RL.3.5
RL.3.7

STORY 10

What a Mess!

Today was an exciting day for Gertrude. She had to stay home alone because I had school, Mom had a meeting to go to, and Mimi had an appointment in the city. The last thing Mom said to me this morning was, "Don't forget to put Gertrude in her crate." Well, guess what I forgot to do? Ugh, I hate when I forget to do things! Gertrude went crazy. The poor little pup! She ripped up my pillows, sending feathers all over the place. She peed on my bed. She ripped my curtains. She ate my cereal, which I left on my dresser. (Yes, Mom has a rule—no food in your bedroom!) Ugh! The worst part of this is that I am to blame for this mess. I should know better. It's going to take a long time for Mom to trust me with the responsibility of having a pet. I have a lot to learn!

STORY 10 QUESTIONS

After you read Story 10, answer the questions below.

1. Who is Gertrude?

_____

2. What did the narrator of the story forget to do?

_____

3. Why does the narrator think it's her fault?

_____

4. Have you ever forgotten to do something that ended up making some sort of mess? What happened?

_____

_____

5. What does it mean to be responsible?

_____

_____

Eating Well at Longwood Elementary

Third graders at Longwood Elementary were treated to a healthy and delicious buffet at lunchtime. It was all part of an effort to get young people to eat more vegetables. The buffet table was filled with colorful dishes. There was a vegetable platter with several different dips to try. There was also a spinach salad. The avocado and tomato plate looked beautiful. The hot foods were brown rice and beans, cauliflower with cheese sauce, and a string bean casserole with mushrooms and onions. For dessert, there was fresh fruit.

What They Ate

- Twyla tasted everything and loved everything, especially the string bean casserole.

- Mahoney only liked the cauliflower with cheese sauce.

- Carmen loved the spinach salad and the avocado and tomato plate.

- Brandon loved the rice and beans but did not like the spinach salad.

- Nico loved the vegetable platter, the brown rice and beans, and the string bean casserole.

- Carlos loved everything and had two plates.

- Mila loved the string bean casserole.

- Winter ate the vegetable platter, the spinach salad, and the avocado and tomato plate. She also really liked the cauliflower with the cheese sauce.

- Finley refused to eat anything, except for a few slices of avocado.

- Paisley tasted everything and loved it all.

	Avocado & Tomato Plate	Brown Rice & Beans	Cauliflower with Cheese	Spinach Salad	String Bean Casserole	Vegetable Platter
Brandon		✓		X		
Carlos						
Carmen						
Finley						
Mahoney						
Mila						
Nico						
Paisley						
Twyla						
Winter						

STORY 11 QUESTIONS

After you read Story 11, answer the questions below.

1.   Who liked everything at the buffet?
   a. Nobody
   b. Paisley and Finley
   c. Twyla and Paisley
   d. Mila

2.   Who ate the string bean casserole?
   a. Paisley
   b. Mila and Paisley and Nico
   c. Twyla, Nico, Carlos, Mila, and Paisley
   d. Finley

3.   What did Winter eat?
   a. The string bean casserole
   b. Rice and beans
   c. the vegetable platter, spinach salad, avocado and tomato plate, and the cauliflower with the cheese sauce
   d. only a piece of fruit

4.   Who ate two plates of food?
   a. Finley
   b. Paisley
   c. Brandon
   d. Carlos

5.   Who liked everything?
   a. Twyla, Carlos, and Paisley
   b. Finley and Carlos
   c. Twyla and Finley
   d. Mila and Carlos

6.   Which dishes were hot?
   a. Brown rice
   b. Brown rice and beans, cauliflower with cheese sauce
   c. Brown rice and beans, cauliflower with cheese sauce, and a string bean casserole with mushrooms and onions
   d. There were no hot foods

I'm Like the Weather

Sometimes the weather is picture perfect. The sky is blue and the sun is shining, and everything looks amazing. But then, almost out of nowhere, clouds come rolling in. Seconds later, the sky darkens, big raindrops hit the ground, and a fierce wind blows everything all around. That is sort of what happened to me last night.

I was playing with friends in my backyard. We were throwing a ball around. My dog Jazz was chasing us, and we were all laughing. I was in the best mood. But then, a bad storm hit inside of me when Zander said, "So, Willy, what time are you going to Shane's party on Saturday?"

"Huh?" I asked. "Shane's party?"

"Yea, it's going to be so fun. Shane's parents are renting a tent," said Zander.

"It is going to be awesome! Everyone is going," Dwayne said.

"I don't know anything about it!" I said.

"Maybe Shane forgot to send you an invite?" Zander said.

How could I not be invited to Shane's party? I thought we were good friends. Last week, me and my dad took Shane to play mini golf.

"The invitation came in the mail like two weeks ago," said Dwayne.

That's when my storm hit. I asked my friends to leave. Jazz started barking and I shouted at him. Then I went to my room.

I threw all my books on the floor. I kicked my closet door. By the time Dad came into my room, my raindrops had started. Not rain, but tears.

Dad asked me what was wrong. I didn't want to say anything. I felt embarrassed, but I was not sure why. What was wrong with me that Shane didn't want me at his party?

Dad told me to come downstairs when I felt like talking. Then he patted my back. I waited until the storm inside of me passed.

When I went downstairs, my clouds had cleared and I told Dad about the stormy feelings I was having. He reminded me that it's okay to have big feelings, and I can always talk to him when it feels like the storm is going to take over.

STORY 12 ACTIVITIES

After you read Story 12, complete the activities below.

1. Pretend that your mood reflects the weather.
   Describe what the weather might looks like to describe the feelings below.
   Is it cold? Hot? Wet? Dry? Windy?

   a. Frightened _____

   b. Sad _____

2. You can help yourself understand your feelings better by creating a feelings wheel. For each "slice," draw a picture of a face that reflects the feeling.

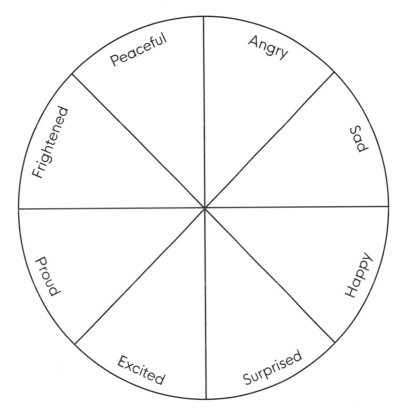

3. What's your favorite feeling and why?

   _____

   _____

   _____

STORY 13 | # The Sauce

The Sauce just opened this week and it is already one of the best restaurants that this town has to offer. The owner, Mason Bushell, says, "The secret to our success is the sauce." Bushell, who has been making his delicious sauce since he was six years old, says, "We use only the best ingredients—the finest tomatoes, the best olive oil, and a few secret ingredients." Bushell says the recipe was passed down to him by his grandmother, Alison Bushell, who worked as an opera singer. "Making sauce every Sunday night with my Gran was the best. We would play music and dance while Gran would mince the garlic and I would peel the tomatoes. Then when we were finished cooking, we would sit and enjoy a bowl of pasta with sauce. So good!" says Bushell.

The dining room at The Sauce is lively and as red as a tomato. One guest was eating a plate of lasagna and said, "This lasagna is the best I have ever had. It's delicious!" Another guest said, "If you don't like tomatoes and tomato sauce, this may not be your favorite place, although the pasta with garlic and oil, no sauce, is pretty good!" If you have not yet been to The Sauce, you must go, and bring the whole family. Kids eat free on Wednesday nights, and on Thursday nights, every table gets a house salad free of charge.

Use the text below to draw the correct amount of tomatoes on the graph for each day. Each tomato represents 1 jar of sauce.

Monday – 3
Tuesday – 5
Wednesday – 3
Thursday – 1
Friday – 7
Saturday – 3
Sunday – 4

MONDAY

TUESDAY

WEDNESDAY

THURSDAY

FRIDAY

SATURDAY

SUNDAY

STORY 13 QUESTIONS

After you read Story 13, answer the questions below.

Use the graph you filled out on the previous page to find the answers to the first 5 questions below.

1. How many jars of sauce were used on Monday?

   _____

2. There were three days that used the same amount of sauce. Which days were they?

   _____

3. Which day used the least amount of sauce?

   _____

4. On which day was the most amount of sauce used?

   _____

5. How many jars were used in total for the week?

   _____

6. What is a key ingredient in the sauce?

   _____

7. On which night do kids eat free?

   _____

Maya's Dream Vacation

For vacation this year, I want to stay in a hotel by the beach. I don't have to stay in a fancy hotel, just a clean room with fluffy pillows and air conditioning. I want the hotel to be close to three good restaurants. I would like to walk a block or two for an ice cream cone. It would be awesome to be able to play miniature golf. I want to go to the beach for most of the day, then run back to the hotel for a shower. For dinner, I would like to go out for barbecue chicken or an eggplant sandwich. I'd like breakfast at the hotel every morning. A bowl of yogurt and some fresh fruit will be just fine. I will sit on the beach and read books, take an afternoon swim, walk along the water, and make a huge sandcastle before getting ready to go to dinner.

Pia's Dream Vacation

This year, for vacation, I want to stay in a hotel with a huge swimming pool. I want a room that faces the water. I want the hotel to be close to at least three good restaurants and lots of shopping. I would like to go to a different fancy lunch spot every day. I am looking to spend most of the day at the pool. Then I would like to be able to take a long walk or a bike ride before taking an afternoon swim. It would be great if the hotel served breakfast every morning. I would like a bowl of yogurt and some fresh fruit.

For Fun! Draw a picture of your dream vacation below.

STORY 14 QUESTIONS

After you read Story 14, answer the questions below.

1. Who wants to stay by the beach?

   _____

2. Who wants to stay in a hotel with a huge swimming pool?

   _____

3. Who wants to play miniature golf?

   _____

4. What do both characters want to do?

   _____

5. Who wants to take a long walk or a bike ride?

   _____

6. Who is looking for a lot of shopping?

   _____

7. Who wants fluffy pillows?

   _____

8. Which vacation sounds better to you and why?

   _____

   _____

   _____

   _____

   _____

   _____

STORY 15 | # Meditate

Meditation—the practice of extended thought, reflection, or contemplation—has been around for thousands of years. It helps people get through stressful times and has lots of healing benefits. Doing it each day for just a few minutes helps create a sense of inner peace. There really is no right or wrong way to do it, but it is a good idea to find a type of meditation that works for you. With mindfulness meditation, you can allow your thoughts to come up, but you don't become involved with them. You can focus on an object, like a doorknob or a light fixture, or even your own breath. You can do this by yourself, without a teacher.

Close your eyes, take a few deep breaths, and concentrate on your five senses. You may choose to focus on your breath or stare at the moon. There are also forms of meditation that allow you to move your body. Sitting upright on the floor is not the only way to meditate. You can lie down, a form of meditation called yoga nidra. With this technique, you pay attention to one body part at a time, leaving you feeling calm. Falling asleep after meditating is not a bad thing. It's your body's way of saying, "Hey, I needed a little rest!" Moving meditation, such as taking a walk around the neighborhood, works if you have trouble sitting still. Short meditation sessions work well. Sometimes, just taking a break from your day for a few deep breaths can help you feel calm.

Definitions

contemplation—looking or thinking about something for a long period of time

reflection—thinking back on something that has already occurred, to learn from experience

STORY 15 QUESTIONS

After you read Story 15, answer the questions below.

1.   How long has meditation been around?
     a. Decades
     b. Hundreds of years
     c. Thousands of years

2.   Sitting upright on the floor is ...
     a. the best way to meditate.
     b. not the only way to meditate.
     c. is not a good way to meditate.

3.   What is yoga nidra?
     a. Yoga that helps you move.
     b. Meditation that lets you lie down.
     c. Meditation while you are asleep.

4.   What can meditation do for you?
     a. It can help you feel calm
     b. It can make you taller.
     c. Twyla and Finley
     d. It can keep you quiet.

 For Fun! Draw a picture of yourself meditating below. What environment are you in? Are you sitting, lying down, or moving?

STORY 16 | # Serious Saturday

Mick and I were jumping on the trampoline when Dad said he needed to tell us something.

"Can it wait, Dad? We are lost in space and a meteor has just exploded—"

"Now!" said Dad.

When we went inside, Dad was on the couch.

"Dad, why are you so serious? It's Saturday," I said.

Dad is usually silly on Saturdays.

"I have news that you may not like."

Mick looked at me as if to say, what is it now?

"Here it is, in a nutshell," said Dad.

"A nutshell? I can't have nuts, Dad!" said Mick.

"Mick, I know you can't have nuts. It's an idiom."

"Okay, lay it on us, Dad!"

"The bad news is, I lost my job. The good news is I got a new job."

Mick and I were quiet.

"The good news is it is a great job!" Dad said.

Mick said, "That's great, Dad. Let's celebrate. I can take you to lunch with my allowance."

Dad smiled.

"The bad news is we are moving across the country. To Idaho!"

"Idaho?" I asked.

"Idaho," Dad nodded. "We move next week."

Mick and I were quiet for the rest of the day.

STORY 16 ACTIVITIES

After you read Story 16, complete the activities below.

Definition

idiom—those funny parts of everyday speech that we use to express our thoughts and feelings without referring to them literally. Idioms are a type of figurative language. In a nutshell is an example of an idiom.

1. Match the idiom to its meaning.

Let the cat out of the bag	Not feeling well
Missed the boat	Raining heavily
Out of the blue	Lost your chance
Piece of cake	Easy
Raining cats and dogs	Sudden surprise
Under the weather	The secret is out

Sample sentences as clues:
- For me, running three miles is a piece of cake!
- Since it's raining cats and dogs, there is no way we can go to the beach!
- He smiled and gave me a cookie out of the blue.

2. Pick two idioms from above and write a sentence that shows that you understand the meaning of the idiom.

_____

_____

_____

_____

_____

_____

"Mind your manners," I tell Theo.

I never thought I would be that person, but Theo really needs better table manners.

When we are at the lunch table, he chews with his mouth open! He also talks and gets food all over his face. Then he wipes it with his sleeve.

"Theo, if you don't get some manners, you are going to be sitting by yourself!" I say.

I am not a mean person. I really like Theo, but his table manners are for the birds.

Things really got bad yesterday, when Theo reached over and took a few crackers off of my plate.

"Whoa, Theo! You cannot do that!" I say.

STORY 17 ACTIVITY

After you read Story 17, complete the activity below.

Circle all of the statements that promote good table manners.

Sit at the table with your hat on your head.

Eat with your mouth closed.

Wipe your hands on the table.

Dive into someone else's sandwich.

Clean up after yourself when you are finished eating.

Don't play with your food.

Keep your napkin on your lap.

Smash your peas.

Don't talk with food in your mouth.

Keep your elbows on the table.

All About Flowers

I absolutely love flowers—daisies, roses, tulips, and daffodils. Flowers make me so happy. Most people see them as decorations for homes and gardens, but did you know that flowers are the part of the plant that makes seeds, which turn into new plants? Flowers get their food from sunlight, water, and minerals in the earth. Without sunlight and water, the plants would die.

Most flowers smell beautiful, but some are actually very stinky. Some flowers can be deadly if eaten. Fun fact: Broccoli is actually a flower.

We have a garden filled with flowers. I painted sunflowers all over my bedroom walls. I am all about flowers. Even my name, Dahlia, is a flower.

STORY 18 QUESTIONS

After you read Story 18, answer the questions below.

1. Flowers are part of what?
    a. The plant that makes seeds.
    b. The plant that makes sense.

2. Where do flowers get their food?
    a. From other flowers.
    b. From sunlight, water, and minerals.

3. What is the narrator's name?
    a. Dahlia
    b. Daisy

4. What is a fun fact that the author includes?
    a. Broccoli is actually a flower.
    b. Flowers need love to grow.

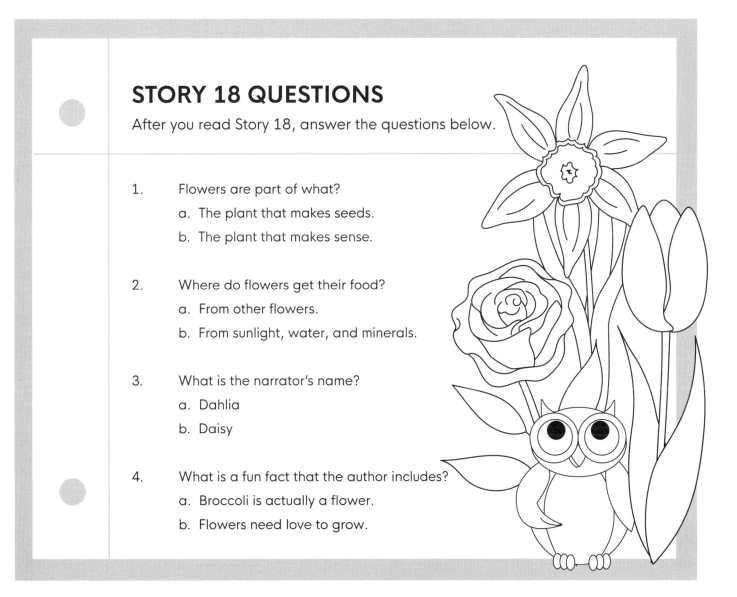

My Bully Day

"Hey, you smell!" says Nisha.

"That's not a nice thing to say," says Pina.

"Nobody is talking to you, Pina. Mind your own beeswax!" Nisha says.

Then Nisha studies me and starts to laugh. "You call those sneakers?" Nisha says. "They look like something my grandmother would wear. Where did you get them? The Loser Store?"

Nisha is the class bully. Today it seems like it is my day to be bullied.

I smile at Nisha and say, "These are my favorite sneakers. I got them in London."

"London? Who do you think you are?" Nisha says with a mean face.

"Yes, London. Have you ever been?" I ask.

Nisha rolls her eyes. "It is talking to me!"

I guess I am an "it" in Nisha's eyes.

"If you don't stop bullying my friend, I am going to get the lunch monitor," says Pina.

"Don't bother," I say. "Nisha can't hurt me."

"Really? Why is that?" she asks me.

"Because I don't pay attention to bullies!" I say.

Then I walk away in my favorite sneakers.

STORY 19 QUESTIONS

After you read Story 19, answer the questions below.

1. Who is the bully?
   a. The narrator
   b. Pina
   c. Nisha

2. What does the narrator say about bullies?
   _____
   _____
   _____

3. Why do you think Nisha might be a bully?
   _____
   _____
   _____

4. What do you think about bullies?
   _____
   _____
   _____

When Little J Threw a Meatball

Little J and her older brother, Sam, fought a lot. He would tease Little J about lots of things—the way she pronounced her "s" sound like an "f" sound, the way she tied her sneakers into knots that she could not un-knot, and the way she bit her nails when she was nervous.

"Leave me alone!" Little J would say.

Her big brother would just laugh at her.

At her Grandpop's birthday party, Little J had had enough of her big brother. They were sitting across from each other at the table in the restaurant, when Sam gave Little J a kick under the table. Little J was so mad, she picked up a meatball from her plate and threw it at Sam, hitting him in the face..

Oh boy, did Little J laugh! Almost everyone at the table laughed. But not Sam, and not Dad. Her dad removed her from the table and went with her to finish her dinner in the car, where he gave her a talk about how to behave in a restaurant.

STORY 20 ACTIVITY

After you read Story 20, complete the activity below.

Pretend you are in charge of telling Little J how to behave in a restaurant.
Make a list of rules for Little J to follow.

One is done for you:

1. When at a restaurant, never throw a meatball at your brother.

2. _____

3. _____

4. _____

5. _____

Time for Allowance

"I want an allowance," I say.

"You're too young!" says Dad.

"But I feel ready!" I say.

"What would you do with the money?" Dad asks.

"I would save some of it," I say.

"You would?"

"Yes. It's important to save for a rainy day!" I say.

"Is that so?" Dad asks.

"Yes!"

"How much money would you want for allowance?"

"My friend Cooper gets $5 a week, but Arthur gets $10," I explain.

"Fine! Here's the deal. We will create a list of chores you can do to earn $6 a week. We will see how it goes," says Dad, reaching for a pencil to begin writing thel list.

STORY 21 QUESTIONS

After you read Story 21, answer the questions below.

1.　　What is an allowance?

_____

_____

_____

2.　　Do you get an allowance?

_____

_____

3.　　If you do get an allowance, do you have to do chores in exchange for the money?

_____

_____

_____

4.　　What do you think is a fair amount of allowance?

_____

_____

_____

5.　　What does it mean to save for a rainy day and why do you think it's important?

_____

_____

_____

6.　　How would having a weekly allowance help you learn to be smart about money?

_____

_____

_____

A New Look for Little J

When Little J turned six, she decided to give herself a haircut. She went into her mommy's sewing closet and found a pair of tiny sewing scissors.

"Perfect! I will give myself the best haircut ever!" Little J said.

She went into the bathroom, closed the door, and locked it. Little J was breaking a rule by locking the door.

"Nobody should lock this door. Ever! We don't need it getting stuck again!" Mommy had said.

But Little J was on a mission. She held the scissors to the top of her head and started cutting and chopping. Little ringlets of dark brown hair fell to the floor. When it was all done, Little J studied herself in the mirror for a long time.

"Hmmm. I am not sure about this look!" said Little J, who now had a row of crooked bangs.

Little J suddenly wanted to run and hide. She put the scissors on the counter and went toward the bathroom door. But the lock was stuck. Little J could not open the door.

"Help!" Little J cried out. "Mom? Dad? I'm stuck in the bathroom and I gave myself a bad haircut!"

It was not a good day for Little J.

STORY 22 QUESTIONS

After you read Story 22, answer the questions below.

1. What did you learn about the character, Little J?

     _____

     _____

     _____

2. Underline the facts in the story based on what you have read.

     • Little J was six when she cut her hair.

     • Little J used her Mom's tiny sewing scissors.

     • When Little J locked the bathroom door, she knew she was breaking a rule.

     • After she cut her hair, Little J left the scissors on the ground.

     • Little ringlets of red hair fell to the floor.

     • Little J looked at herself in the mirror for a long time.

     • Little J suddenly wanted to run and hide.

3. How would you end Little J's story? Write it here:

     _____

     _____

     _____

     _____

     _____

     _____

     _____

     _____

     _____

     _____

     _____

Save the Planet

In 2019, Greta Thunberg sailed on a yacht to talk about climate change in New York. Greta is an activist who speaks out against companies that are destroying our planet. Greta, who was born in 2003, is autistic, a disability she has described as her "superpower."

World temperatures continue to rise, as a result of humans using too much oil, gas, and coal. When these fuels burn, they release gasses into the air. The gasses trap the sun's heat in the earth's atmosphere and cause the planet's temperature to rise. Our oceans and habitats are in danger. In a warmer world, animals will have trouble finding food and water. Polar bears may be wiped out because the ice they rely on is melting. Scientists warn that at least 550 species may be lost in this century if something is not done.

What can you do about climate change? Experts say to limit airplane rides, use electric cars or no car at all, ride a bike, eat less meat, buy energy efficient products, and insulate your home.

STORY 23 ACTIVITY

After you read Story 23, complete the activity below.

Match the question with the answer from the text.

What did Greta do in 2019?	Autism
When was Greta born?	Humans using gas, oil, and coal
What disability does Greta have?	Ride a bike
How is climate change caused?	Spoke about climate change
What happens when the fuels burn?	2003
What can you do about climate change?	They release gasses into the air.

Who was Amelia Earhart?

Amelia Earhart believed that women could do anything that men could do. Born in 1897, she was the first woman to fly across the Atlantic Ocean and to fly nonstop across the U.S. in 1932. She was an American aviator who worked as a nurse's aide in World War I. She bought her first airplane at the age of 24. Earhart was the founder of the Ninety-Nines, an organization for female pilots. She flew in the first Women's Air Derby in 1929. Sadly, Earhart and her plane went missing in 1937.

In a letter to her husband, she wrote about the risks of flying. "Women must try to do things as men have tried. When they fail, their failure must be but a challenge to others."

STORY 24 ACTIVITY

After you read Story 24, complete the activity below.

Underline the facts from the passage.

Amelia Earhart was born in 1897.

Amelia Earhart was the kindest woman.

During World War I, Amelia Earhart worked as a nurse's aide.

Amelia Earhart was the smartest nurse in the war.

Amelia Earhart took her first solo flight in 1921.

Amelia Earhart bought her first plane at the age of 24.

It must have been terrible when Amelia Earhart's plane went missing.

Amelia Earhart was a very brave woman.

Kiran Helps a Friend

I am Kiran. I have a best friend, Pearly. She is a unicorn, and nobody can see her but me.

My favorite thing to do is play fashion show. Pearly and I love to dress up and walk the runway!

"Hi friends, I am Pearly the unicorn," says Pearly.

"I am Kiran: fashionista, big sister, friend to all animals, and everybody's favorite lunch date!" I say to my pretend audience.

This is my good friend, Drake. Drake is seven now, just like me, so we are practically grown-ups. We usually talk about everything—from Pearly, to puppies, to how to make a yummy smoothie.

Drake worries. A lot. About everything. Today he is particularly worried that his birthday party is not going to be fun.

"It will be awesome!" I say. "Don't worry!"

But Drake worries that his guests won't come to the party. He worries that he won't be a good host. He worries that the cake won't be delicious.

Poor Drake.

"Slow it down, Drake!" I say.

I take Drake's hand and we sit down for a minute. Then we take some slow, deep breaths together. Soon, Drake is calm.

"Let's pose like brave warriors!" I say.

Drake and I pretend that we are fearless tigers. Then we roar.

Now Drake is feeling strong and ready to talk about his birthday party.

"It's going to be lots of fun!" I say.

"I know!" says Drake.

STORY 25 QUESTIONS

After you read Story 25, answer the questions below.

1. Circle the main idea of this story from the choices below.
   a. You can help yourself make your worries go away.
   b. Worrying is good for you.
   c. Worrying means you care.
   d. All of the above.

2. Why is Drake particularly worried today?
   a. His clothes do not fit.
   b. He is worried about his birthday party.
   c. He cannot see Pearly.
   d. He is afraid of tigers.

3. In the story, what does the word particularly mean?
   a. Especially
   b. Invisible
   c. Anxious
   d. None of the above

4. What does Kiran do to help Drake with his worries?
   a. She takes Drake's hand.
   b. They take a few deep breaths together.
   c. They pose like brave warriors.
   d. All of the above.

5. How do you get rid of worries?

   _____

   _____

   _____

   _____

   _____

   _____

Worry Dolls

Today at school, I made a worry doll. I used a wooden clothespin for the body and then wrapped colorful thread around it. Using markers, I drew two eyes, one nose, and a mouth, and then cut yarn for hair and glued it to the top.

Worry dolls come from a country called Guatemala. According to legend, a worry doll is a small friend who can carry big problems. If you tell your worry doll all your worries before bedtime, the doll will take each worry away.

I am worried that. . .

nobody will sit with me at recess.

I will not be able to hit the ball with the bat.

my grandmother is very sick.

I will need glasses.

my dad will be mad when he finds out I lost my bracelet.

Then I put my doll under my pillow. During the night, while I sleep, my worry doll takes away all of my worries.

STORY 26 ACTIVITY

After you read Story 26, complete the activity below.

What Happens When

After reading about worry dolls, can you put these directions in order?
The last one is done for you.

- ◯ Put it under your pillow.

- ◯ Tell the doll all your worries.

- ◯ Draw a face on it.

- ◯ Cut yarn for hair.

- ◯ Find a clothespin.

- ◯ Glue the yarn to the top of the clothespin.

- ◯ Go to bed.

- ◯ Wrap the clothespin with colored yarn.

- ⑨ Wake up without worries!

 For Fun! Try making your own worry doll! Use the illustration on page 52 to inspire you.

Supplies you'll need:
- wooden clothespin
- colorful embroidery thread
- markers
- yarn
- glue

Gloria Takes a Break

Gloria had so much to do.

Too much to do for just one cat.

Gloria had lots of responsibilities.

She was in charge of the family business and the family.

She was in charge of cooking, cleaning, sewing, and more.

She had to step in when the kitties were fighting.

She stepped up when her family needed something.

But now, Gloria was feeling tired.

She needed peace and quiet.

A friend called Gloria, and said to her:

"Make time for self-care.

It's only fair.

Gloria, you have a full plate!

Some of these things will have to wait.

You need some time for you.

What I'm saying is true.

Take a nap in the sun.

Take a walk, or even a run.

Clear your day and stroll in the park.

Tell yourself jokes in the dark.

When was the last time you just sat?

Relax, you way-too-busy cat!"

Gloria changed her ways and took time for herself.

Gloria was now a happy cat!

STORY 27 ACTIVITY

After you read Story 27, complete the activity below.

Word Find Find these words from the story.

Gloria	busy	happy	
cat	relax	sun	self

```
G L O R I A E T
C N O D B U S Y
A Q S H W T I N
T H A P P Y N A
N X A L E R A I
E S E L F C H L
T O N W S U N O
```

STORY 28 | # Baby's First Laugh

When a Navajo baby is about three months old, the family starts thinking about the baby's first laugh.

A Navajo baby's first laugh is a special ceremony that welcomes the child into the Navajo community. The person who makes the baby laugh has the joyful task of providing a feast for the baby's entire family.

At the celebration, the guests eat rock salt as a reminder that humans are connected to the earth. It is also a reminder of a time when salt was hard to come by. The salt represents hope that the baby will grow up to be generous and joyful. Then, the baby is given a gift of turquoise jewelry. The baby wears the beautiful blue stone as protection.

This ceremony, called *A'wee Chi'deedloh*, is the first big milestone in a baby's life. At the end of the party, the baby gives small bags of candy, money, and other gifts, and the guests wish the baby a long and generous life.

For Fun! Create an illustration to go with the story above.

STORY 28 QUESTIONS

After you read Story 28, answer the questions below.

1. What is a *A'wee Chi'deedloh*?

    a. A ceremony celebrating baby's first cry.

    b. A ceremony celebrating baby's first laugh.

2. Who is responsible for throwing the party?

    a. The Navajo community.

    b. The person who makes the baby laugh.

3. Why does the baby have to wear turquoise?

    a. It protects the baby.

    b. The turquoise looks nice on the baby.

4. Why do the guests eat rock salt?

    a. It is a reminder of when salt was hard to come by.

    b. The Navajo people like salt.

5. What happens at the end of the party?

    a. The guests dance and laugh.

    b. The guests wish the baby a long and generous life.

Pizza, Pizza!

Today, after school, we made our own pizza, and it was the best thing I have ever tasted. I have always liked pizza, but I have never loved it the way some people do. Pizza is what my family eats when we don't have much time. Every Wednesday, I have to be on the field to play baseball by 6 p.m. Those are the best pizza nights. My mom or dad will order a plain pizza with a side salad. It's always tasty, though not my favorite meal by any means. But today, all of that changed. Everyone got to make their own small pizza. We put a pinch of flour on a tray so the dough would not stick. We were each given a piece of dough to roll out. Then we dressed it up with sauce, cheese, and lots of toppings. There was spinach, pineapple, ham, black olives, red pepper slices, and onions. My pizza had just a little sauce and a mountain of cheese, and my toppings were spinach, peppers, and onions. When it came out of the oven, it was bubbly and so delicious. Pizza is my new favorite food!

 For Fun! Create an illustration to go with the story above.

STORY 29 QUESTIONS

After you read Story 29, answer the questions below.

1. How does the author enjoy eating pizza?

   a. By making it himself

   b. By ordering it from a restaurant

2. When does the author's family eat pizza?

   a. When the author's mom is craving pizza

   b. When the author's family has a busy evening

   c. When the house is a mess

3. Why does the author add a pinch of flour to the tray?

   _____

4. What toppings does the author add to his pizza?

   _____

   _____

5. Ask five friends what their favorite pizza topping is. Write the results here:

   1. _____

   2. _____

   3. _____

   4. _____

   5. _____

Letter from Camp

Dear Mom, Dad, Kiki, and Lukey,

Hi everyone! I am having fun at camp, but I miss you very much—even you, Kiki. Who would have thought I would miss my little sister? Lukey, I miss you the most. It is hard to fall asleep without your yucky dog breath in my face. Just kidding. Not really.

Dad, I am learning archery, and this afternoon I am taking a paddle boat out for a spin with this kid named Wheels. I don't know if that's his real name, but it is what everyone calls him. I will try to get someone to take a picture of me on the boat so you can add it to the photo wall.

Mom, can you make me your specialty? You can send the plain banana bread without the chocolate chips so it won't melt. The truth is the food here is pretty gross and I am hungry most of the time. In fact, maybe you can send zucchini bread along with the banana bread.

 **For Fun!** Create an illustration to go with the story above.

STORY 30 QUESTIONS

After you read Story 30, answer the questions below.

How do you know?

After you read the letter, think about what you can infer from the words that the letter writer uses. Match each statement with its correct support statement.

Statements

1. Lukey is a dog. _____

2. Wheels may or may not be his name. _____

3. The letter writer is the older sibling. _____

4. Mom is very good at making banana bread. _____

5. Dad collects photos. _____

Choose from these support statements:

a. You can add it to the photo wall.

b. I don't know if that's his real name, but everyone calls him that.

c. It is hard to fall asleep without your yucky dog breath in my face.

d. Who would have thought I would miss my little sister?

e. You can send the plain banana bread without the chocolate chips so it won't melt.

No More Quitting

I'm Quinn. I like to start things, but I don't always finish them. I start a hobby, then I get bored. Piano lessons. Got bored. Guitar lessons. Got bored. Singing lessons. Got bored. Quinn the Quitter. That's me. So, when I asked my mom if I could take art classes, she looked at me hesitatingly.

"Quinn," Mom said. "I just don't think you have found something that you will stick with. All these lessons cost money!"

I know money doesn't grow on trees. It would be awesome if it did. I could try things out and not worry about wasting money if I didn't want to stick with them.

But, just between us, I do feel differently about art lessons. I really want them. I love drawing and all my friends say I am really talented. My teacher was the one who suggested that I take art classes.

"Mom," I said. "This is different. I really love art. I'm good at it and I want to become an artist."

Mom studied me.

"Quinn," Mom finally said. "That makes sense. We can sign you up for art classes if you commit to finishing all of them and not quitting mid-way."

"Yippee! I promise I won't quit this time!" I said, giving Mom a hug. "How about we go shopping for art supplies?" I asked with a wink.

Then Mom said, "Now you're pushing it! How about you go clean your room?"

STORY 31 QUESTIONS

After you read Story 31, answer the questions below.

1.   Who is the main character in the story?

_____

2.   Why doesn't Quinn continue with new hobbies?

_____

3.   What new hobby is Quinn particularly interested in?

_____

4.   Why is Quinn excited about the new hobby he wants to try?

_____

5.   Why does Quinn's mom hesitate when he asks about his next hobby?

_____

Answer the questions below all about YOU.

6.   What special activities interest you?

_____

_____

_____

7.   Have you ever started something—a book, an art project, a sport, a class—and then become bored with it and wanted to quit? Why?

_____

_____

_____

8.   What is one activity you would really like to do?

_____

_____

_____

Circle of Compliments

My friends and I played a game called "Circle of Compliments." Everyone sat in a circle, and I handed my friend Beau a small drum.

"Beau," I said, "While you hold this drum, I want you to give everyone in the circle a compliment."

"Wait," said Feebee. "What's a compliment, again?"

"You have beautiful eyes, Feebee," I said.

"Oh, thanks, but what is a compliment?" Feebee asked.

"You have beautiful eyes!" said Beau.

"Oh, thank you! But what is a compliment?"

"Feebee, that is a compliment!" I said.

"Oh!" Feebee nodded. "Now I get it!"

"A compliment is a polite expression of praise," I say.

Beau holds the drum and delivers compliments to everyone in the circle. Then, Feebee holds the drum and doles out her compliments. After we give each other compliments, we felt happy.

 For Fun! Create an illustration to go with the story above.

STORY 32 QUESTIONS

After you read Story 32, answer the questions below.

Do you like to give and receive compliments?

1. What is the best compliment that you ever got? Who gave it to you?

    _____

    _____

    _____

2. What is the best compliment that you ever gave someone else?

    _____

    _____

    _____

3. Think of five friends. Write a compliment for each friend.

    _____

    _____

    _____

    _____

    _____

    _____

    _____

    _____

Do a Dumb Thing

Did you ever do something dumb? You don't know why you did it. It makes no sense. But somehow you did it and somebody got mad. Well, that's what happened to me. I was playing outside by myself. Maybe I was in a bad mood because my mom took my sister shopping, and I was not allowed to come because I still had homework to do. I was outside with my big box of colored chalk. I was drawing flowers all over the driveway when I saw a familiar car. It was Rosey, my mom's best friend and her whole family. Rosey's husband honked the horn, and I looked up at the car. Rosey was waving and her kids were in the backseat waving, and her dog, Murphy, was barking. That's when I did the really dumb thing. I stuck my tongue out at them! I didn't smile or wave, just stuck out one long, red tongue.

Rosey called my mom and told her that I had done something rude.

When my mom asked me why I did it, I shrugged my shoulders. "I don't know why I did it. I wasn't feeling like myself."

STORY 33 QUESTIONS

After you read Story 33, answer the questions below.

1. Did you ever do something you know was wrong, but for some reason you did it anyway? What could you have done differently?

   _____

   _____

   _____

2. Do you think the person in the story should apologize to Rosey and her family? Why or why not?

   _____

   _____

   _____

A Couch to Remember

When the Barry family moved to Ferry Cove, they were sad to leave the life they had. They lived in a house along the river for many years, but a fire broke out when the family was at a town parade and the house burned to the ground. The Barry family lost everything. When they moved to Ferry Cove, people who had heard about the fire donated some furniture and clothing for them. Someone donated a big red couch.

One night when Sofia and her brother Clyde were on the couch, their dog Clifford jumped on the couch and started sniffing around. When Sofia stuck her hand under the couch cushion, she could not believe what she found: a big, fat pile of $100 bills. Sofia shouted for her parents, who came running, thinking that something was wrong. When they saw the money, they called the Ferry Cove police department. The officer in charge told the Barry family that they were honest people for checking on it, and if they could not find the person who had given away the couch, then they could keep the money.

STORY 34 QUESTIONS

After you read Story 34, answer the questions below.

1. Where did the Barry family move to?

   _____

2. What happened to the Barrys' house along the river?

   _____

   _____

3. What did Sofia find under the couch cushion?

   _____

4. Why did the Barry family contact the police?

   _____

   _____

5. What is the name of Sofia's dog?

   _____

6. Do you think this story has a happy ending? Why or why not?

   _____

   _____

Dear Diary

My mom has superpowers. She is a healer and I want to be just like her.

We were at Tim's house today and I had a chance to see Mom in action. While Tim and his dad, Mr. Wixley, were standing near the barbecue, Mom was talking to me and Mrs. Wixley. I was about to ask Tim if he needed help setting the picnic table, when all of a sudden, Mr. Wixley lost his balance and fell to the ground. He was not breathing.

"Mom!" I yelled.

Mom, who is a doctor, ran over and within seconds, was pressing her hands on Mr. Wixley's chest.

"Kathleen!" Mom called out to me. "Call 911!"

By the time the ambulance came, Mr. Wixley was breathing.

As Mom drove us home later that night, I told her how awesome I think she is.

 For Fun! Draw a picture of someone in your life who is a superhero.

STORY 35 ACTIVITY

After you read Story 35, complete the activity below.

Write a diary entry about someone you know who has a superpower.

Dear Diary,

_____

_____

_____

_____

_____

_____

_____

_____

_____

_____

_____

_____

_____

_____

_____

_____

_____

STORY 36 | **Scrap**

Scrap was a dog who lived on his own because his master had died the previous winter. Now Scrap ran through the woods at night trying to find scraps to eat. During the day, he would sleep in front of the old shack where his master had lived. Scrap was tough, but he was always hungry. He had become so thin and weak in recent days. As he made his way through the brush, he heard barking.

A beautiful Golden Retriever spoke first. "Hello?" he said.

But Scrap was so weak that he just fell in a heap.

"Come, let's take care of him," said a black poodle.

So, the two dogs gathered a water jug and a big bowl of kibble. They placed it in front of Scrap, who started eating right away.

The two dogs, who looked healthy and handsome, had chains around their necks. Scrap was curious.

"What's with the chains?" Scrap asked, after he had eaten all the food and drank all the water.

"Our master chains us so we don't run away," the poodle said.

"But our master is a kind and gentle soul. Would you like to meet him? I am sure he would let you stay with us." said the Retriever.

Scrap thought about it. He could be free but hungry, or he could be well-fed and chained. It was a difficult choice for Scrap.

STORY 36 QUESTIONS

After you read Story 36, answer the questions below.

1. What would you do if you were Scrap?

   _____

   _____

2. Create a list of 3 reasons for Scrap to stay free.

   1. _____

   2. _____

   3. _____

3. Create a list of 3 reasons for Scrap to stay with the two dogs and their master.

   1. _____

   2. _____

   3. _____

   ⭐ **For Fun!** Create an illustration below to show Scrap's decision.

STORY 37 | # Who Were The Brothers Grimm?

We have Jacob Grimm and his brother Wilhelm to thank for so many well-known tales, such as *Rapunzel*, *Cinderella*, and *Snow White.* But who were these men? The Grimm brothers were librarians in the early 19th century who did not actually write the stories for which they are known. Instead, they collected those stories and turned them into local folklore. The brothers interviewed friends and relatives and wrote down their stories. The collection, known as Grimm's Fairy Tales, contains more than 200 stories, including *The Frog Prince*, *Little Red Riding Hood*, and *Hansel and Gretel*. It has been translated into more than 160 languages! Many of these stories have been made and remade into movies. Even though many people would consider them children's stories, they were not originally meant for kids. The fact that the tales were intended for adults explains why the stories were much darker and scarier than the versions we know today.

For Fun! Create an illustration for your favorite Grimm's fairy tale.

STORY 37 QUESTIONS

After you read Story 37, answer the questions below.

1. How many languages have the stories been translated into?

   _____

2. How many stories are in the collection?

   _____

3. What is your favorite Grimm's fairy tale and why?

   _____

   _____

   _____

4. Think of a good family story. Write it down using as much detail as possible. Then read it aloud to friends.

   _____

   _____

   _____

   _____

   _____

   _____

   _____

   _____

   _____

   _____

   _____

   _____

   _____

Letters Between Friends

Dear Avril,

      This is a letter of apology. I really was planning on taking you to the lake house with my family next weekend. But what happened was that me and my mom ran into Sienna and her mom at the House of Sneakers. We were talking, and then my mom went ahead and invited Sienna and her mom to the house! There was nothing I could do. As you know, the house is really small. I should have told you right away, but I felt so bad about un-inviting you (is that even a word?) that I thought it was better to just ignore you. It was not a nice thing to do. I talked to my mom about it and she said that she didn't know I was planning on taking you. She said that you are welcome to come with us next month. That's when we are going to the lake house for four full days, and it will be warmer so we can definitely swim. Please forgive me, Avril. I never meant to hurt your feelings. You are my very best friend. Will you please forgive me?

From,

Kate

Dear Kate,

      Unfortunately, this is not the first time that you have done this to me. Last year, I was all set to go to the water park with you, and the day before we were supposed to go, you said you were sick. But I know you were not sick. You went to the water park with Cleo. I do forgive you, but I am not comfortable saying yes to your invitation. I belive that being a good friend means being honest. I am not mad at you, but I would prefer not to go to the lake house with you.

From,

Avril

STORY 38 QUESTIONS

After you read Story 38, answer the questions below.

1. What did Kate do wrong?

    _____

    _____

    _____

    _____

    _____

2. How should Kate have handled the situation after her mom invited Sienna and her mom?

    _____

    _____

    _____

    _____

    _____

3. Do you think Avril and Kate will be friends again? Why or why not?

    _____

    _____

    _____

    _____

    _____

A Rough Summer

My name is Max and the summer I turned 7, I was having scary thoughts. Monsters, people dying, rats crawling across my belly. It was awful. I couldn't turn it off. Most nights, I would wake up cold and sweaty with a pounding heart. Unable to go back to sleep, I would cry. By the time morning would come, I would be so tired.

When my teacher told my mom that I was having trouble concentrating at school, she suggested I see Dr. Peter. The first time I met him, he sat across from me and set up a game of chess. As we played the game, he asked me questions about my life.

This is what I learned about myself: I was angry that my dad was gone a lot. I was afraid that if something happened to my mom, I would be alone.

Dr. Peter helped me feel better with these tips:

When I feel nervous, I can just take five minutes to sit and breathe. In and out. Nice, deep breaths.

When something is upsetting to me, I can talk to my mom, my teacher, Dr. Peter, or a friend.

When I feel sad, I can draw or write in a journal.

If I need help, I can do some positive talking to myself like this: "I am a good, strong, and happy person. I have a lot to offer the world. I am smart, kind, and a good friend."

STORY 39 QUESTIONS

After you read Story 39, answer the questions below.

1. What is the narrator's name?

    _____

2. What kind of thoughts was the narrator having?

    _____

3. Based on what you have read, how do you know Dr. Peter is trying to help Max?

    _____

    _____

    _____

4. Why do you think the narrator and Dr. Peter played chess?

    _____

    _____

    _____

5. Why was the narrator afraid that he would be alone?

    _____

    _____

    _____

6. Have you ever tried any of Dr. Peter's tips when you feel worried?

    _____

7. If yes, which ones work for you?

    _____

    _____

    _____

Jack's the Winner

"Jack, you can't always win!" I shout.

"Yes, I can!" says Jack.

"I'm serious!" I say.

"Me too!" says Jack.

The fact is, Jack is only happy when he wins. If we are in the middle of Monopoly or chess and Jack is afraid that he might lose the game, he says the game is over. That's the worst.

I will be one move away from winning, and Jack will say, "No fair! I'm not playing anymore."

So I have decided that I am not playing any more games with Jack.

Not until he proves that he can lose a game graciously.

Definitions
graciously—in a courteous, kind and pleasant manner
humble—courteous and respectful

For Fun! Create an illustration that shows gracious losing and humble winning.

STORY 40 QUESTIONS

After you read Story 40, answer the questions below.

1. What is Jack's problem?

    a. He does not like to win.

    b. He does not like to lose.

    c. He is a big baby.

2. What games does the author mention?

    a. Video games

    b. Monopoly and chess

    c. Monopoly and card games

3. Do you know someone like Jack?

    a. Yes

    b. No

4. What are some ways you can help a person who doesn't like to lose become more gracious?

    _____

    _____

    _____

    _____

    _____

5. Why do you think Jack doesn't like to lose?

    _____

    _____

    _____

    _____

Meet Grandma Moses

Have you ever heard of Grandma Moses? She was a famous folk art painter. Born on September 7, 1860, Anna Mary Robertson was one of ten children in her family. At the age of 12, she left her home to become a farmhand.

She married a man named Thomas Moses in 1887. They lived in Virginia in the beautiful Shenandoah Valley. Then the couple moved to a farm in New York.

As a child, she drew pictures and colored them with the juice of berries. The artist grew up and didn't start painting seriously until she was in her seventies.

In 1939, Grandma Moses had some of her paintings hanging in a drugstore window, when an art collector named Louis Caldor bought all of them. The paintings were pictures of life on a farm. Later that year, the paintings were on display at the Museum of Modern Art in New York City.

Throughout her life, Grandma Moses painted about 2,000 paintings. She died in 1961.

STORY 41 QUESTIONS

After you read Story 41, answer the questions below.

1. What is the real name of Grandma Moses?

    a. Mary Ann

    b. Anna Mary (Robertson) Moses

2. When she was a child, what did she use to create art?

    a. The juice of berries

    b. Crayons and markers

3. How many paintings did Grandma Moses create?

    a. 100

    b. 2,000

4. What was the name of the art collector that bought Grandma Moses' paintings?

    a. Louis Caldor

    b. Thomas Moses

5. How old was the artist when she left home to work on a farm?

    a. 12

    b. 61

Goodbye Zelda!

From the age of three, Zelda and I were the best of friends. Her family moved into the house next door before we could even walk. Our moms drank herbal tea and did yoga in the mornings, while Zelda and I played in her tiny sandbox. Since Zelda's mom is a professional singer, she would sing to us all the time. I had a tambourine and Zelda had a drum, and we would pretend to be in a band with Zelda's mom. My mom would take pictures of us performing. Mom has more than a hundred pictures of us playing in the backyard.

As the years passed, Zelda and I stayed close. We enjoyed sports, music, ballet, and cooking. Zelda and I have the same favorite food (pizza). We even have the same birthday, so celebrating has always been double the fun.

But two weeks ago, Zelda and her family moved to upstate New York, where Zelda's mom is going to open a singing club. I am happy for Zelda, but sad for me. I miss her a lot.

For Fun! Create an illustration of one of the scenes in the story above.

STORY 42 QUESTIONS

After you read Story 42, answer the questions below.

1.   What is the central idea of this story?

     _____

     _____

     _____

2.   Why is the narrator sad?

     _____

     _____

     _____

3.   What instruments did the narrator and Zelda play?

     _____

4.   Do you have a close friend who you grew up with?

     _____

5.   Share five facts about your friend.

     1.   _____

     2.   _____

     3.   _____

     4.   _____

     5.   _____

Self-Care for Young People

Here is a list of ways young people can take care of themselves:

Enjoy the sunshine

On the next sunny day, take a walk, run, or bike ride. Isn't it wonderful to have such a beautiful day with your favorite person?

Make Your Own Grateful Jar

Place a jar by your bed. Every morning write something you are grateful for on a strip of paper and fold it up until it's tiny. Then put it in the jar. Read the contents of the jar whenever you need cheering up

Walk Out

Walking is the most natural form of exercise and it's good for you. Walk around your neighborhood with a four-legged friend or a friend from school.

Happy Hour

Have your family host a virtual party with relatives who live far away. Tell jokes and stories. Ask questions.

Picture It

Have your family dress up for a fancy photo shoot. Have the people in your family take turns being in front of the camera.

Make a Wish List

What hobby would you like to pursue? Skiing? Jewelry making? Creating an herb garden? Make a list and take steps to try out one or two items on your list every few months.

Wear It

Do you have a piece of clothing—a belt, vest, cape, hat, or scarf—that you love? Wear it today and really stand out.

Take a Trip

Go somewhere without leaving your home! Take a virtual tour of the Eiffel Tower, Yellowstone National Park, or the Bronx Zoo.

Sleep

Take a nap. Just an hour to close your eyes, relax, and ... zzzzzzzzzzzzzzzz.

Practice Positivity

What makes you happy? Puppies and kittens? Family and friends? A tree house? Journal all about it.

STORY 43 QUESTIONS

After you read Story 43, answer the questions below.

It is important to take care of yourself!

1. Which of these ideas have you already tried?

   _____

   _____

   _____

2. Which idea appeals the most to you and why?

   _____

   _____

   _____

3. Why do you think it is important to take time to enjoy life?

   _____

   _____

   _____

 **For Fun!** Create an illustration of your favorite self care idea.

Yesterday we had this awesome substitute teacher. She asked us to share some of our most embarrassing moments with the rest of the class. At first, nobody wanted to share and there was total silence. But then, the teacher told us her embarrassing story. She was in a writing contest and she thought she heard her name when the winner was announced, so she rushed up on the stage to accept the award ... only to find out that she was not the winner! It was another person who had a similar name as her. She was so embarrassed!

Soon, everyone in the class wanted to share their embarrassing stories. We were all laughing, but not in a mean way at all. It was so fun. I shared the story about when I forgot to take the price tag off my new outfit and the whole day I walked around with tags hanging off my shirt. Then, I shared the time that I accidentally ate dog food because I thought it was leftovers from my favorite restaurant. I also shared the story about how I came out of the bathroom and my shirt was tucked into my underwear and I didn't even know! Ugh, so embarrassing.

What we learned is that everyone gets embarrassed at some point in their lives. Sometimes it's easy to shake off an embarrassing moment, and sometimes it's not. For some kids, the fear of being embarrassed can lead to negative feelings. The teacher taught us that it's important not to tease someone when they feel embarrassed.

STORY 44 QUESTIONS

After you read Story 44, answer the questions below.

1. Which title do you think is best for this piece?
   a. Most Embarrassing Moments
   b. Yikes! I'm Embarrassed
   c. Everyone Gets Embarrassed

2. Share an embarrassing moment here:

   _____

   _____

The Right Dog for Me

I used to have a little dog named Lulu. I loved her so much. She was small and cuddly, and I loved the way she would fit in my lap. Lulu died last year. It was very sad, but my parents said that she had lived a nice, long life.

Two months ago, Dad brought home another puppy for me and my brother Kippy. We were so excited to meet the pup, but when Dad brought Rascal home, he was huge and wild. The first day I met him, he bit me about four times. Each time, it was just a nibble, but still, it was a bit scary. Lulu would never bite, but Rascal was different. Also, Rascal and his tail were already so big, that whenever he would get close to me, he would accidentally knock over my bowl of cereal or my cup of almond milk. Kippy loved Rascal right from the beginning. He wanted a big dog, but I needed time to adjust. I needed some quiet time with Rascal. I wanted to make sure that Rascal could be gentle with me. After a week of keeping my distance from Rascal, he came into my room early one morning. He jumped up on my bed, and just when I said, "No, Rascal," he cuddled next to me and fell asleep in my arms. Hours later, Dad was rushing around the house yelling, "Where's Rascal?"

"He's in here with me!" I yelled.

That's when I knew that Rascal would be my dog forever.

STORY 45 ACTIVITY

After you read Story 45, complete the activity below.

Read the statements below. Underline only the ones that are facts.

Lulu died last year.

Lulu was the best dog that ever lived.

Two months ago, the narrator got a new dog.

Kippy loved Rascal right from the beginning.

Rascal was the scariest dog that ever lived.

When the narrator first met Rascal, he was bitten four times.

The narrator needed some time to adjust to Rascal.

Rascal was the cuddliest dog.

Grab a Sandwich!

The fourth Earl of Sandwich invented the sandwich in 1762. According to legend, the earl loved to play cards. Whenever he was hungry, he slapped a hunk of roast beef between two slices of bread so that he could hold his food in one hand and continue his card game without having to leave the game to eat a meal. The eleventh Earl of Sandwich opened a chain of sandwich restaurants called Earl of Sandwich. The chain has more than 30 locations in the United States. This earl says he does not enjoy a sandwich that is too big or overstuffed with everything in it. He prefers a simple sandwich cut in a triangle shape. He thinks that a wrap is not a sandwich, and does not know why the fish sandwich is not a more popular choice.

For Fun! Read the words in each of the columns to make a delicious sandwich by using 2 or more items from each column. Then give your sandwich a name. Draw a picture of your sandwich on the next page.

Bread	Cheese & Meat	Toppings	Spreads
White bread	Swiss cheese	Lettuce	Mayonnaise
Wheat bread	American cheese	Oickles	Mustard
Hard roll	Cheddar cheese	Onions	Ketchup
Soft roll	Turkey	Tomatoes	Oil and vinegar
Croissant	Roast beef	Salsa	Salt
Baguette	Tuna	Avocado	Pepper
Bagel	Meatball	Roasted peppers	Tomato sauce
Hawaiian roll	Ham	Herbs	Hummus

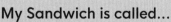

My Sandwich is called...

STORY 46 QUESTIONS

After you read Story 46, answer the questions below.

1. What did the Earl of Sandwich invent in 1762?
   a. Card games
   b. Mayonnaise
   c. The sandwich

2. According to legend, why was the sandwich invented?
   a. So the earl did not have to stop his card game to eat.
   b. So the earl could become famous.
   c. So the earl could eat without a plate or napkin.

3. What is the name of the more than 30 sandwich restaurants?
   a. The Sandwich Shop
   b. Wrap and Roll
   c. Earl of Sandwich

 Draw a picture of your favorite sandwhich below.

The Iditarod

The world's most famous sled dog race is called the Iditarod. The race takes place every year in March in Anchorage, Alaska. The race is hard for both the sled driver and their dogs. The sport challenges contestants to keep moving for more than a thousand miles. The pathways are freezing and snowy. There are usually about fifteen dogs per sled in the race.

The first official Iditarod, which was shorter than it is now, took place in 1973. However, the first notable dog sled races happened between 1908 and 1917, on a 408-mile course. Perhaps the most well-known sled dog event was in 1925, when a relay race of sled drivers and their dogs traveled through blizzard-like conditions in order to transport a life-saving medicine.

The whole community celebrates Iditarod week with activities, educational talks, concerts, dances, and sports competitions. Today, technology makes it easy for onlookers to track the racers.

 For Fun! Create an illustration to go with the story above.

STORY 47 ACTIVITY

After you read Story 47, complete the activity below.

Word Find Find these words from the story.

Alaska	dog	sled	race
blizzard	Iditarod	sport	

I D I T A R O D

C E S D L U S O

A L P R A C E G

T S O P S Y O A

N X R L K R A L

E S T L A C H A

B L I Z Z A R D

Make Time for Sports

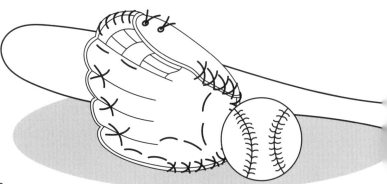

Playing sports is a smart idea for many reasons. First of all, sports are fun, and they are a great way to make fitness a part of your life. By being involved in a sport at a young age, you have more of a chance to be active at an older age. The other great thing about sports is that it teaches the importance of teamwork. You also learn how to follow directions and become a leader.

Studies have shown that if you are good at sports, you are often also good at school. In addition, studies show that playing a sport can help a young person release stress and tension. You don't have to be the best player on the team. You just have to try your best. Being involved in sports is also a great way to make friends! That is a great reason to pmake time for sports.

STORY 48 QUESTIONS

After you read Story 48, answer the questions below.

1. What is one reason sports are a smart idea?

   _____

   _____

   _____

2. What are two things studies show about sports?

   _____

   _____

   _____

The Right Sport

"Get up and move!" your parents tell you. But what is there to do that will burn energy and be fun? Try any of these sports to see what feels right to you. In the past, kids would play their own versions of games like Hide and Seek or I Spy. But today's kids need more structure in their day. So, what are the top sports for kids today?

Football is a popular game that can be played as young as age four. It helps build flexibility, muscle, and all-over fitness.

Swimming is a fun sport that can really strengthen your lungs and muscles. How about riding your bike? Excellent choice. Cycling strengthens your legs, improves balance, and helps keep your heart strong.

Inline skating is fun, but it can be expensive. It's a popular sport that is really great for balance.

What can you do with a ball and a hoop? Play basketball, of course. Dribbling the ball will help you improve your eye-foot coordination.

Some kids like to play one sport; while others like to play as many as they can. What about you?

STORY 49 ACTIVITY

After you read Story 49, complete the activity below.

There are a lot of sports to try. Look at the list of sports. Draw a circle around each sport that is mentioned in the text.

dribble	skiing	baseball
football	inline skating	soccer
basketball	bike riding	running
surfing	swimming	

Oops, I Made a Mistake

Oh no, you spilled your milk. No sense crying over it! You accidentally dropped your book on your foot and hurt your big toe. You made a mistake and took home someone else's sneakers. You lost your house key on the first day it was given to you.

You make mistakes. We all do. Forgot your library book again? Your teacher may tell you that if you cannot remember to bring back your library book, you will not be able to borrow another one.

What could you do? Write yourself a note to bring the book back and tape it to your front door? Yes. Put the book in your backpack the night before? Yes! When you figure out a way to fix a mistake, you will feel successful. You have just learned from a mistake. Hooray for you!

Mistakes. Who needs them? We all do. Nobody likes making mistakes, but we learn from them. Mistakes teach us that nobody is perfect. Not many people can set a goal and simply achieve it. We have to practice, make mistakes, and keep our eye on the prize.

Making mistakes helps us solve problems. Mistakes teach us lessons. Sometimes, making a mistake has a positive outcome.

 For Fun! Create an illustration showing you fixing a mistake you made.

STORY 50 QUESTIONS

After you read Story 50, answer the questions below.

1. What is a mistake?

_____

_____

_____

_____

_____

2. Describe a mistake you made.

_____

_____

_____

_____

_____

3. How did you fix it?

_____

_____

_____

_____

_____

4. What did you learn from it?

_____

_____

_____

_____

_____

STORY 1: MISSY AND THE SCARF

1. Missy

2. Missy's House

3. 2

4. She does not like strawberries

5. Answers will vary.

6. What happened when sequencing:

- **6** The girls began playing Hide and Seek.
- **5** Missy put on her scarf.
- **4** Auntie Maggie showed up.
- **3** A package came.
- **2** The girls were washing their hands.
- **1** The girls were making banana bread.

STORY 2: LET'S WORK TOGETHER

1. Because he has a point

2. Because he is colorful

3. Answers will vary

4. Answers will vary

STORY 3: MAKE TIME FOR POSITIVE MESSAGES

1. Themself

2. Finds a quiet space

3. They are okay with who they are.

4–5. Answers will vary

STORY 4: SASSY AND EVER

Fact or Opinion?

A Sassafras tree can have colored leaves. **(F)**

Evergreens are the most beautiful trees. **(O)**

The leaves on Evergreen trees are always green. **(F)**

Most children prefer trees with colorful leaves. **(O)**

Fall is the most wonderful time for trees to show off. **(O)**

Sitting under a Sassafras can improve your mood. **(O)**

Fact or Opinion?

Tree populations are declining. **(F)**

Trees produce oxygen. **(F)**

Trees with red leaves look best. **(O)**

Trees should be planted in the early morning. **(O)**

When planting trees, always wear gardening gloves. **(O)**

STORY 5: WILLOW AND MA

1. **a**   2. **b**   3. **c**   4–5. **Answers will vary.**

STORY 6: PLAY IT!

1. **c**   2. **a**   3. **b**   4. **a**   5. **a**

STORY 7: CHICKEN MAKES QUESADILLAS

1. **a**   2. **b**   3. **a**   4. **c**   5. **c**

STORY 8: LARGE SIDE OF OPTIMISM

1. **b**   2. **c**   3. **a**   4. **b**

STORY 9: DOG WEARING A PIZZA BOX

1. Ringo
2. Big
3. For an operation
4. The cone
5. Pizza
6. The pizza box

STORY 10: EATING WELL AT LONGWOOD ELEMENTARY

1. **c**   2. **c**   3. **c**   4. **d**   5. **a**   6. **c**

STORY 11: I'M LIKE THE WEATHER

Answers will vary.

STORY 12: THE SAUCE

1. 3
2. Monday, Wednesday, Saturday
3. Thursday
4. On which day was the most amount of sauce used?
5. 26
6. Tomatoes
7. Wednesday

STORY 13: SUMMER VACATION DREAMS

1. Maya
2. Pia
3. Maya
4. Go swimming, Have breakfast: yogurt and fruit each morning
5. Pia
6. Pia
7. Maya

STORY 14: WHAT A MESS!

1. The dog
2. She left the crate open.

3–5. Answers will vary.

STORY 15: MEDITATE

1. **c**   2. **b**   3. **b**   4. **a**

STORY 16: SERIOUS SATURDAY

Let the cat out of the bag: **the secret's out**

Missed the boat: **lost your chance**

Out of the blue: **sudden surprise**

Under the weather: **not feeling well**

Piece of cake: **easy**

Raining cats and dogs: **raining heavily**

STORY 17: WHERE ARE YOUR MANNERS?

Eat with your mouth closed.

Keep your napkin on your lap.

Don't talk with food in your mouth.

Clean up after yourself when you are finished eating.

Don't play with your food.

STORY 18: THE PERFECT GIFT

1. **a**   2. **b**   3. **a**   4. **a**

STORY 19: MY BULLY DAY

1. c

2. She doesn't pay attention to bullies

3–4. Answers will vary.

STORY 20: TIME FOR ALLOWANCE

1. Allowance is money that a kid receives from their parents each week.

2–6. Answer will vary.

STORY 21: NEW LOOK FOR LITTLE J

2. Underline the facts in the story based on what you have read.

Little J was six when she cut her hair.

Little J used her Mom's tiny sewing scissors.

When Little J locked the bathroom door, she knew she was breaking a rule.

Little J suddenly wanted to run and hide.

STORY 22: WHEN LITTLE J THREW A MEATBALL

1. Answers will vary.

STORY 23: SAVE THE PLANET

1. Spoke about climate change

2. 2003

3. Austism

4. Humans using gas, oil, and coal.

5. They release gasses into the air.

6. Answers will vary. Example: Ride a bike rather than drive a car.

STORY 24: WHO WAS AMELIA EARHART?

Underline the facts from the passage:

Amelia Earhart was born in 1897.

During World War I, Amelia Earhart worked as a nurse's aide.

Amelia Earhart took her first solo flight in 1921.

Amelia Earhart bought her first plane at the age of 24.

STORY 25: NO WORRIES FOR KIRAN

1. **a**   2. **b**   3. **a**   4. **d**   5. **Answers will vary.**

STORY 26: THE GIFT / WORRY DOLLS

Put it under your pillow. **(7)**

Tell the doll all your worries. **(6)**

Draw a face on it. **(3)**

Cut yarn for hair. **(4)**

Find a clothespin. **(1)**

Glue the yarn to the top of the clothespin. **(5)**

Go to bed. **(8)**

Wrap the clothespin with colored yarn. **(2)**

Wake up without worries! **(9)**

STORY 27: GLORIA TAKES A BREAK

Word Search Answer Key

STORY 28: BABY'S FIRST LAUGH

1. **b**   2. **b**   3. **a**   4. **a**   5. **b**

STORY 29: PIZZA, PIZZA

1. **a**   2. **b**

3. A pinch of flour will prevent the dough from sticking.

4. Cheese, spinach, peppers, and onions

STORY 30: LETTER FROM CAMP

1. **c**   2. **b**   3. **d**   4. **e**   5. **a**

STORY 31: NO MORE QUITTING

1. The main character is Quinn.

2. Quinn gets bored with every hobby he has tried.

3. Quinn is excited about art lessons.

4. Quinn loves to draw, he's good at it, and his teacher suggested he take art classes. He is being encouraged to try art classes.

5. Quinn's mom is hesitant because all of the hobbies Quinn tried in the past he wanted to stop doing them.

6–8. Answers will vary.

STORY 32: CIRCLE OF COMPLIMENTS

Answers will vary.

STORY 33: DO A DUMB THING

Answers will vary.

STORY 34: A COUCH TO REMEMBER

1. Ferry Cove

2. The house burned down.

3. A pile of $100 bills.

4. The family called the police because they wanted to do the right thing

5. Clifford.

6. Answers will vary.

STORY 35: DEAR DIARY

Answers will vary.

STORY 36: SCRAP

Answers will vary.

STORY 37: WHO WERE THE BROTHERS GRIMM?

1. The stories have been translated into more than 160 languages.

2. There are more than 200 stories in the Grimm's collection.

3–4. Answers will vary.

STORY 38: LETTERS BETWEEN FRIENDS

Answers will vary.

STORY 39: A ROUGH SUMMER

1. The narrator's name is Max.

2. Max was having dark thoughts.

3. Max says Dr. Peter helped him feel better.

4. They played chess together to get to know each other.

5. After his dad left, Max thought if something happened to his mom, he would be alone.

6–7. Answers will vary.

STORY 40: JACK'S THE WINNER

1. **b**   2. **b**   3–4. **Answers will vary.**

STORY 41: MEET GRANDMA MOSES

1. **b**   2. **a**   3. **b**   4. **a**   5. **a**

STORY 42: GOODBYE, ZELDA!

1. The narrator is telling about her longtime friend, Zelda.

2. The narrator misses Zelda.

3. The narrator played the tambourine and Zelda played a drum.

4–5. Answers will vary.

STORY 43: SELF-CARE FOR YOUNG PEOPLE

Answers will vary.

STORY 44: TOO EMBARRASSED TO SPEAK

Answers will vary.

STORY 45: THE RIGHT DOG FOR ME

Lulu died last year.

Two months ago, the narrator got a new dog.

Kippy loved Rascal right from the beginning.

When the narrator first met Rascal, he was bitten four times.

The narrator needed some time to adjust to Rascal.

STORY 46: GRAB A SANDWICH!

1. **c**   2. **a**   3. **c**

STORY 47: THE IDITAROD

STORY 48: MAKE TIME FOR SPORTS

Answers will vary.

STORY 49: THE RIGHT SPORT

The sports mentioned in the story:
football
basketball
inline skating
bike riding
swimming

STORY 50: OOPS, I MADE A MISTAKE!

1. A mistake is something that is wrong or goes wrong, often because of lack of knowledge or a misunderstanding.

2–4. Answers will vary.

READING SKILLS

Reading: Literature

RL.3.1
Ask and answer questions to demonstrate understanding of a text, referring explicitly to the text as the basis for the answers.

RL.3.2
Recount stories, including fables, folktales, and myths from diverse cultures; determine the central message, lesson, or moral and explain how it is conveyed through key details in the text.

RL.3.3
Describe characters in a story (e.g., their traits, motivations, or feelings) and explain how their actions contribute to the sequence of events.

RL.3.4
Determine the meaning of words and phrases as they are used in a text, distinguishing literal from nonliteral language.

RL.3.5
Refer to parts of stories, dramas, and poems when writing or speaking about a text, using terms such as chapter, scene, and stanza; describe how each successive part builds on earlier sections.

RL.3.6
Distinguish their own point of view from that of the narrator or those of the characters.

RL.3.7
Explain how specific aspects of a text's illustrations contribute to what is conveyed by the words in a story (e.g., create mood, emphasize aspects of a character or setting).

RL.3.9
Compare and contrast the themes, settings, and plots of stories written by the same author about the same or similar characters (e.g., in books from a series).

RL.3.10
By the end of the year, read and comprehend literature, including stories, dramas, and poetry, at the high end of the grades 2–3 text complexity band independently and proficiently.

Reading: Informational Text

RI.3.1
Ask and answer questions to demonstrate understanding of a text, referring explicitly to the text as the basis for the answers.

RI.3.2
Determine the main idea of a text; recount the key details and explain how they support the main idea.

RI.3.3
Describe the relationship between a series of historical events, scientific ideas or concepts, or steps in technical procedures in a text, using language that pertains to time, sequence, and cause/effect.

RI.3.4
Determine the meaning of general academic and domain-specific words and phrases in a text relevant to a grade 3 topic or subject area.

RI.3.5
Use text features and search tools (e.g., key words, sidebars, hyperlinks) to locate information relevant to a given topic efficiently.

RI.3.6
Distinguish their own point of view from that of the author of a text.

RI.3.7
Use information gained from illustrations (e.g., maps, photographs) and the words in a text to demonstrate understanding of the text (e.g., where, when, why, and how key events occur).

Reading: Foundational Skills

Read with sufficient accuracy and fluency to support comprehension.

RF.3.4.A
Read grade-level text with purpose and understanding.